Noritake Collectibles

Lou Ann Donahue

Wallace-Homestead Book Company
1912 Grand Avenue
Des Moines, Iowa 50305

Published by

authoritative books on antiques & collectibles

Wallace-Homestead Book Company
1912 Grand Avenue
Des Moines, Iowa 50305

CONTENTS

ACKNOWLEDGMENT

I am grateful to the Noritake Company Inc. for their co-operation in providing information and pictures. Their contribution has greatly enriched this book.

Photographs by Thoen Photography, Minnetonka, Minnesota.

Backstamps were hand-drawn by Lou Ann Donahue.

FOREWORD

This book is to help collectors satisfy their curiosity for detailed information on old dinnerware patterns in Noritake and to present a guide to the backstamps and the relative value of Noritake collectibles.

Please note that I say collectibles, for these china pieces are collector pieces and not true antiques. These beautiful china pieces of a bygone era are today's collectibles.

Noritake china, from its Nippon period up through the 1930s, has become a collecting phenomenon. People are buying Noritake today as a hobby, as an investment or simply because they enjoy the memories of the old designs. The vase that sat in grandmother's cabinet and gathered dust has automatically gone up in value. No one knows exactly why, but beauty, scarcity and artistry have much to do with the value placed on old Noritake china.

There seems to be some confusion in the interchangeable use of the words china and porcelain. The word porcelain came from the latin word porcella, meaning seashell. The word china came from the country of its origin, China. I will use china throughout this book as it seems to be favored in the United States, while porcelain seems to be used more in Europe. Both words describe the same delicate product.

I hope this book will make collecting Noritake an exciting hobby for you. Information was gained in bits and pieces, from Noritake records, English translations of old Japanese writings and interviews with Noritake Company personnel. Dates of important historical events were verified by encyclopedia.

The wares photographed throughout the book are from my own private collection.

— Lou Ann Donahue

HISTORY OF NORITAKE

The Noritake Company, operating under the name of Nippon Toki Kabushiki Kaisha Ltd., was founded in January 1904 at its present site in Nagoya, Japan, located on the main island of Honshu.

Prior events that eventually led to the development of the Noritake Company began with the history of Japan's export trade during the 17th century. During this century, Japan was under a repressive system of feudal government that suppressed economic progress. All trade with foreign countries was prohibited, except for a Dutch trading post. While the trading nations extended their empires, Japan remained a closed nation.

In 1839, Baron Ichizaemon Morimura was born in a family of merchants who acted as purveyors to the feudal lords. Shortly after, in 1854, an American officer, Commodore M. C. Perry, delivered a letter requesting the opening of trade to the Emperor of Japan from President Franklin Pierce. Commodore Perry returned one year later and signed a limited trade agreement with Japan.

In 1859, a delegation, which included the Baron Morimura, was sent to the United States to return the courtesy visit of Commodore Perry to the Japanese shores. Before leaving Japan, the delegation had to change their Japanese money into American money in the Yokohama foreign concession. The gold coin of Japan was exchanged for the silver coin of the United States. Baron Morimura felt that it was a loss to Japan to allow gold of such high purity to flow out of Japan in this way. He spoke about that matter with Yukichi Fukuzawa, one of the leaders in the modernization of Japan from the feudal shogunate governing era. Fukuzawa told Morimura it was necessary to promote export trade so that the gold coin that went out of Japan would flow back into the country. The delegation was impressed with the market for Japanese products in the United States.

The imperial capital of Japan was transferred in 1868 from Kyoto to Tokyo, where it remains today.

In 1876, Baron Morimura founded Morimura Bros., Inc. at the Ginza in Tokyo. He started as a trading firm in exporting the traditional Japanese style of potteries, bamboo works and other Japanese gift items. By 1877, Morimura Bros., Inc. had trading offices in New York and were importing the finest quality of chinawares. Japan strived to adopt the techniques of the Western world. Chinaware was designed with an appeal to the taste and lifestyles of the United States market.

Japan was rapidly transformed into an industrial country. During Japan's expansion of export business, the Morimura Bros., Inc. decided to concentrate on ceramics and saw the need for a factory in Japan that would produce chinaware designed especially for the United States market. Thus, Noritake was founded on January 1, 1904. The founders of the company were Baron Ichizaemon Morimura, Mogobei Okura, Jitsuei

7

Hirose, Kazuchika Okura, Yasukata Murai and Kootaro Asukai. The location of the factory, at the present site of the main factory, was near the supplies of raw materials and in the area of the most skillful potters. This location insured that Noritake would produce chinaware worthy of the Morimura family insignia.

During 1907, Noritake began producing grinding wheels and machines for use in its own china factories. Development of these grinding wheels was an important factor in the growth of the china industry, since it would have been impossible to master the techniques to manufacture high quality chinaware without them.

At the beginning, Noritake made such items as coffee sets and dressing table sets, and later the elliptic shaped plates and large round serving plates. Designs of these earlier pieces were mainly a gold line rim with fruits, flowers and foliage in low relief or inlay. Later designs sometimes used transfer paper made in England or France to give a European flair to the patterns.

In November 1910, a prince who later became the Emperor Taisho of Japan, visited the Noritake factory and ordered dinnerware for his royal affairs. Later, the Emperor and Empress ordered Noritake dinner sets for an Imperial dinner.

Noritake had orders from prominent families, people who traveled Europe and the United States and others who studied abroad. One of the orders of that era was a dinner set which was not an American style, but was a gorgeous and gigantic set consisting of 172 plates.

Other special orders began arriving. Noritake, in 1911, had a special contract with the Japanese Navy for dinnerware that was delivered to each naval station.

The five department stores in Japan in 1911, whose major business was to sell groceries, also sold some Noritake china.

A big event occurred in 1914 when the first dinnerware pattern, number D1441, was produced for export to the United States. From personal conversation with a present Noritake Company executive who saw a picture of this pattern, it was learned that the pattern had a cream-colored band with small floral designs on the rim. Up to this time, all dinnerware produced by Noritake was sold within Japan.

Noritake soon received many orders from hotels and restaurants in Japan. They delivered dinnerware, with the pattern of autumn flowers, to the Imperial Hotel in Tokyo. Later, in 1916, Frank Lloyd Wright, the famous American architect who was in charge of remodeling the Imperial Hotel, designed a pattern of light blue circles for its dinnerware. This dinnerware was then produced by the Noritake Company. Noritake's dinnerware soon was used by the Mikado, Kanaya and Nikko Hotels, and many others in Japan, Korea and Taiwan.

Noritake's Okura China was first produced in 1919 in the suburbs of Tokyo by Magobei Okura and his son, Kazuchika, who were also founders of Noritake. They were seeking to create the most beautiful and highest quality of china. It was soon realized that they had succeeded. Most of the Okura art valued in the United States is in the form of beautiful vases, but in Japan it is the Okura dinnerware that is highly revered. It is made of highly refined materials and fired at exceptionally intense heat for strength and durability. It was, and still is, exquisitely hand-decorated by highly skilled Japanese artists. The Japanese artist's position was an honored one, and inventiveness of design was prized. The artist could not always produce the lightness of his Chinese inspiration, but he always kept in mind the treasured heritage of craftmanship that was handed down through the generations. Noritake's artists developed beautiful artworks and unique glazing processes that produced a color as fiery red as the setting sun.

Until about 1921, Noritake used the word "Nippon" to mark its wares that were exported from Japan. Nippon is a name for Japan, derived from Dai Nippon, meaning Great Japan. The expression came from the Chinese for the place of the rising sun. But the United States congress passed a law in 1921 making it compulsive that all imports must have the country of origin marked in the English language. So, thereafter, all Noritake wares exported to the United States stated on their backstamps "Made in Japan" or "Japan".

Politics in the 1920's in Japan were dominated by big business. Trade and industry continued to expand. Business was interrupted by an earthquake in 1923 that destroyed much of Tokyo and Yokohama.

In the early years of Noritake, the production of blanks, which were unpainted wares, played an important part in the export trade. The blanks were painted by hand in many different areas, so that the quality of the finished wares varied from mediocre to excellent and rich in gold trim. The blanks carried a backstamp with both words "Noritake" and "Nippon" separated by a curved line. You may find these wares in antiques stores today.

Mass production of Noritake china became possible because they could form the clay with a jigger mold. Small quantities of clay were put into jigger molds and formed into exact shapes. The excess was cut off the outside of the mold. Finishing the china wares, such as scraping and smoothing, had to be done by hand. But the early use of the jigger mold helped make possible the production and export of large quantities of chinaware.

Noritake made other than chinawares. During the 1930's, the gypsum shop of the Noritake factory, which

11

produced plaster of paris, became a separate division named Nitto Sekko Kaisha Ltd. of Japan.

On December 7, 1941, Japan opened hostilities against the United States and England by striking Pearl Harbor. Warfare reached Japan itself with intensive bombing. The main chinaware factory in Nagoya was seriously damaged. Equipment and raw material resources were bombed. The number of employees was reduced from 4,000 to 1,000. In 1945, the atomic bombs were dropped on Hiroshima and Nagasaki which led to Japan surrendering in Tokyo Harbor on September 2, 1945. Many of the Noritake Company's records were destroyed during World War II, but chinaware production did not stop.

After World War II, the United States 8th Army and the Allied Occupation Forces, who knew the quality of Noritake china, came to Japan and set up a procurement office to supply the needs for their troop housing program. To comply with this demand, which was large enough to rehabilitate the factory, Noritake continued to manufacture chinaware. The company had the assistance of GHQ Industrial Division, Aichi Prefectural Military Government, QMC of Tokai Region. Others also helped Noritake obtain such raw materials as fuels, liquid gold and packing materials, and also issued to Noritake huge blanket orders which allowed for financing and recovery.

However, in 1946 and 1947, Noritake did not supply chinaware to United States military personnel under the "Noritake" brand name, but used instead the name "Rose China". The reason for this name change was that Noritake could not produce up to the same standards of pre-war high quality because of a shortage of superior raw materials, equipment and skillful employees. The company did not want to spoil the high reputation of the Noritake name established in pre-war days in the United States. The United States Army Procurement Office understood the situation and accepted the "Rose China" chinaware until 1948.

In 1947, the Central Purchasing Office was established in Japan and started distributing Noritake China to Rycom, Philcom, Marbo and all other United States Exchanges in the Far East. Since then, Noritake has been supplying their china to the United States Military PX's.

Ushiro Saegi, president of Noritake after World War II, put a great emphasis on quality and producing china for the life styles of the importing countries.

In November, 1947, Noritake, Inc. of the United States was organized in New York. Other offices were opened throughout the states from 1960 through 1970.

In the course of Noritake's growth, the company has expanded its activities to produce crystal glassware, melamineware and stainless steel flatware.

Today, Noritake has established many manufacturing plants as joint-venture companies with such overseas areas as Iran, Sri Lanka, the Philippines and Colombia. A new arrangement in Ireland established Noritake Ireland in 1977. The yearly worldwide sales for all Noritake affiliates amounts to nearly $200 million.

Noritake manufactures more china dinnerware than any other company in the world. Among the monthly output of over five million pieces of chinaware, about 70 percent is exported to more than 90 countries.

Top row, left: Ichizaemon Morimura, founder of Noritake Company Inc.

Top row, right: Magobei Okura, founder of Okura Art China and an executive of the Noritake Company Inc.

Bottom row: Frank Lloyd Wright plate, designed for the Imperial Hotel in Tokyo, Japan.

森村市左衞門

大倉孫兵衞

NORITAKE — NIPPON WARES
(1891-1921)

The last quarter of the 19th century was noted by the opening of an import office in New York by the Morimura Brothers of Japan. They began to import Japanese chinaware into the United States in a limited amount. With improvements in manufacturing methods came increased production and increased importing of chinawares.

The Nippon era began in 1891 when the word "Nippon" was printed on all imported wares from Japan. The highly protective McKinley Tariff Act, passed in October, 1890, stated that wares imported into the United States must bear the name of the exporting country. Noritake used the Japanese name for Japan, which was Nippon, to mark their wares until 1921.

Chinaware imported by the Morimura Bros. Inc. also bore a backstamp for identification. Backstamps used were mostly symbols so they could be understood by everyone. Some backstamps are identical except for different colored inks. The reader may wish to refer to the chapter on backstamps for those used by Noritake during the 30-year Nippon era.

Collecting Noritake-Nippon wares requires a familiarity with the quality of the china and the distinctiveness of the artwork. Knowledge of this kind should create a respect for the fine brush strokes of each design and an admiration for the hours of workmanship put into each piece of china.

Collectors are now buying the Noritake-Nippon finer and older wares. This activity has put these wares into the classification of best sellers, and prices have risen rapidly in recent years.

Plate #1
Noritake-Nippon

Top Row:

Tea Strainer. Fine translucent china. Heavy encrusted gold trim in a variety of designs. (1) green.*

Dish, 3x6¼", satin finish. Decorated with gold beaded border. Painted a pale yellow with a hunting scene, an Indian in a canoe with gun and a moose in the woods near the water. (1) green.

Vase 6". A creamy background with gold trim on bottom, pure white background with pink flowers on top. Twin gold handles. One piece. (1) green.

Ring Tree. Brown bracelet on stem. Brown border with pink flowers and a sailboat around base. (1) green.

Middle Row:

Water glass and covered pill box. Pure white background with purple, brown and gold trimmed flowers. Dark brown stripe border. Very translucent. (1) green.

Bowl 8" diameter. Gold beaded border with geometric and bird designs in lilac, red and black. Excellent detail. Inside background pale yellow with an Indian in canoe hunting moose. Large gold loop handles. Satin finish. (1) green.

Vase 5¾". Satin finish. Muted scene of a house and trees. Twin handles in gold. (1) green.

Bottom Row:

Planter. An unique item. A lovely light blue background color, raised white designs of flowers. This item resembles some Wedgwood pieces and is referred to as Wedgwood-Nippon. (1) green.

Box, round 2". Satsuma-style decorated with cobalt blue, green and brown raised enamels. Cover has two figural Japanese men. Entire box covered tiny enamel dots. (1) blue.

Vase 4¾". Decorated with a landscape with the usual house motif. Twin handles with raised brown trim. (1) green.

Vase 6". Brown satin finish background. Yellow and blue flowers with iris-type leaves. Twin gold handles, six ball feet. (1) green.

*Note — The number in parentheses refers to a particular back-stamp shown in the chapter on backstamps, pages 68-88. The backstamp given is for the particular ware as pictured. The color refers to the color used in the backstamp.

Plate #2
Noritake-Nippon

Top Row:

Bowl 5¼". Brown shaded background with a cluster of gooseberries. Dark brown fluted edge. (1) green.

Plate 7¾". Brown tone acorns with green leaves. Lilac landscape in middle of plate. (1) green.

Bowl 2½"x6¾". Brown tones with acorns and leaves. Gold handles. White outside. (1) green.

Middle Row:

Condiment Set — Six pieces. Tray 5½"x7¼". All pieces are heavily encrusted with gold flowers and leaves. Lid of mustard jar has gold finial. (1) green.

Bottom Row:

Bowl 6¼". Gold stripe and raised beading around inside. Dainty blue and pink flowers circle bowl. Gold medallion center. (1) magenta.

Dish, small. Yellow background with house and bridge in a wooded area. (1) green.

Bowl 6¼", footed. Pure white china with pink apple blossoms and a pair of blue birds with tan breasts on branch. A touch of spring. It has a 1¼" footed base. (1) green.

Plate #3
Noritake-Nippon

Top Row:

Cake Plate 9" with 1" slant sides. Outside border is tan with greek key pattern in gold. Below that, a one-inch band of rust and green geometric flowers, followed by another band of tan and gold. Two gold handles. Unusual colors for Nippon wares. (1) green.

Vase, round 4". White background with light brown top, three curved feet and handles. Four flowers front and single flower back. Scalloped mouth with dark brown edge. (1) green.

Dish 7¼". Light blue border with pink bell-type flowers with blue stamen all around border. Gold edge with pierced handles. (1) green.

Middle Row:

Vase 7¼". Background is an off-white with pink colored mums and variegated green leaves. Top and bottom has black and gold outlined windows. Tiny opening at the neck, possibly to be wired for a small lamp or used for a single-stemmed flower. Complete design is outlined in gold. (1) blue.

Butter pat 3¼". One of set of six. Gold trim on a cream border. Tiny pink flowers. One of the early dinnerware patterns produced by Noritake. (6) green.

Bowl 8¾", 8-sided. Encrusted gold designs on a pure white background, trimmed with pink and green jewels. Gold medallion center. Very ornate. (2) red and green.

Wall Plaque 5½". Olive green, satin finish, border with black, red and white geometric designs. Center design depicts two sailboats with violet sails and in the background a windmill. (1) green.

Bottom Row:

Bowl 5" square. Pastel yellow background. Beautiful pink roses inside with single bud. Square opening on top with round base. Unusual shape. Gold edge. (1) green.

Bowl 5"x9". Pure white background with cobalt blue geometric design, light blue trim and tiny pink, red and yellow flowers in border. Large pierced handles. Gold edge. (3) blue.

Dish 2½", pedestal base. Panels of light blue and green alternate with pink around inside border. Raised designs in black enamel on each panel. Center design in olive green, light green and pink. Gold handles. Very interesting design. (4) green.

NORITAKE — JAPAN WARES
(1921—present)

The words "Made in Japan" or "Japan" began to appear on wares imported from Japan in 1921 because "Nippon" was no longer acceptable. During the early 1920's, some china wares were marked with both "Japan" and "Nippon", but Noritake Inc. did not use this double marking system.

One of the most innovative looks of the period was luster wares. Luster china was manufactured extensively by the Noritake Company from about 1921 to the middle 1930's. Art Deco followers will find much to collect from the Luster period. The reader may wish to refer to the chapter on Luster.

Transfers were used during this period to decorate the china. Transfers were a universal blessing, for they allowed the public to buy beautiful dinnerware designs that would have been extremely expensive if produced by all hand painting. The most artistic transfers were of a neutral color outline, filled-in with color by hand, the highlights touched up with white paint and the rims hand-painted in gold.

The occupation of Japan by the Allied Occupation Forces, from late 1945 to early 1952, required that the backstamps of china ware bear the words "Made in Occupied Japan". Production was limited, but many pieces of this chinaware can be found in this country today. Gold and silver banding on the rims and raised design were hand painted.

Beginning in the 1950's, Noritake produced a variety of ornamental art pieces such as figurines and vases and other products for better home living.

Collectors can obtain these Noritake-Japan pieces without spending a lot of money and enjoy the charm and workmanship of each ware. Because many of these wares were painted with some hand work and represent a nostalgia for the past, collectors are scrambling for these wares.

Plate #4
Noritake-Japan

Top Row:

Cheese and Cracker Server, 8¾". One piece. Blue border with black geometric panels and pink flowers between panels. Gold trim. (9) green.

Spoon Holder 2¼"x8". Black and gold border. Cream and white background with a pair of flowers on each side of center. Gold trim on handles. (9) green.

Bowl 5¼", footed. Pastel lilac background with a large white swan in water with woods behind. Black scalloped edge. Three white ball-shaped feet. (9) green.

Dish 5¾" square. Black border of gold leaves. One-inch band of pink decorated with yellow flowers and blue leaves. Pierced handles. (9) green.

Middle Row:

Bowl 6" square. Black border with white center. Variety of flowers in pastel colors. (9) green.

Coffee set, Demitasse. 14 pieces. All are decorated with dark orange background with a stylized phoenix bird on a branch with flower blossoms. Gold handles and finial on coffee pot. Set does not contain a creamer. (9) green.

Bottom Row:

Child's China set, service for two, 12 pieces. Light blue and black border. Center design is a dark brown basket with flowers. Set includes 2 cups and saucers, 2 dinner plates, 1 cake plate, 1 teapot, 1 soup tureen, and 1 large platter. (9) green.

Plate #5
Noritake-Japan

Top Row:

Plate 6¼". Cobalt blue border with gold leaves. Panels of pastel colored flowers on peach background. White center. (9) green.

Cream and Sugar set. Cream background with grey stripe decorated with pink roses. No cover on sugar. Silver handles and trim. (9) red.

Bowl 8"x9½". A scenic piece with colorful violet orchid sky with large trees, and in the far distance a windmill. Outside border and single handle are gold. (9) green.

Vase 6¾". A black background with gold dots in sets of three covering vase. On front are four peony-type flowers with two flowers on back. Gold band on mouth and twin handles. The entire vase has a high gloss finish. (9) green.

Middle Row:

Mustard Jar. Bright yellow background with two tomato-type fruits on front. Black trim. (9) green.

Candy Dish. A garland of roses on a shaded pastel background. Gold trim on center handle. (9) red.

Dish 4¼" x 5½". Orange sunset with trees in fall foliage, and small house. Single pierced handle. (9) green.

Plate. Orange to yellow sky with green foliage on trees. Cabin by lake. (9) green.

Bottom Row:

Bowl. Modern design of a bird. Bright yellow, orange and green geometric shapes. One-inch sides. Unusual design. (9) red.

Nut Bowl set. Walnut texture to outside of all pieces. Well-painted walnuts inside each piece. Satin finish outside and gloss finish inside. (9) green.

Candy Dish 3¾"x6¼". Straight sides with irregular shape to edge. Stippled turquoise background on sides. Center handle. (9) green.

Plate #6
Noritake-Japan

Top Row:

Berry set. Large bowl and six sauce dishes. Cream colored border with yellow and black geometric design below border. Center floral design. (9) red.

Condiment set, six pieces. Very popular "Roseara" pattern. Tray, salt and pepper and mustard pot. (10) red.

Candy Dish. "Roseara" pattern. Green border followed by black and white thin stripe. Next is a cream band with four floral garlands. Center handle is gold trimmed. (10) red.

Middle Row:

Bowl. Round 6½". Twin gold bow-shaped handles. Tan border with three floral design and three diamond designs. White center. (9) green.

Nut Bowl set, scalloped gold trim edges. Cream colored border with flowers. Pure white center. Three raised feet on each piece. (9) green.

Plate. Three-sided with three pierced handles. Green border with tropical garden design of flowers and a parrot on branch in center. Gold leaves. (9) red.

Bottom Row:

Basket. Cream colored background with stylized flowers. Gold handle and trim. Six tiny feet. (9) red.

Demitasse Cup and Saucer. Pure white background with tiny pink roses and grey leaves. (16)

Plate 6¼". Imari-type design. Colors used are cobalt blue, orange and gold on a white background. (9) green.

Relish Dish. Twin-sided. Green stippled border outlined in gold on both sides. A large group of flowers on one side are balanced by two smaller groups of flowers. Large gold handle. (9) red.

Compote. Same design as above in relish dish. Pedestal base. (9) red.

AZALEA

A favorite dinnerware pattern and most sought after among collectors is Azalea. Azalea (tsutsuji in Japanese) is a delightful pattern with exotic, orchid-like, trumpet shaped azalea flowers in shades of red and pink with green leaves on a white background.

The Larkin Company of Buffalo, New York, which manufactured Sweet Home Soap, played a major role in presenting Noritake china to the United States. Larkin offered premiums with the sales of their soap, and in 1901 founded the Buffalo Pottery Company to produce wares for premiums in their catalogs. Among the most collectable of the wares made by the Buffalo Pottery Co. was Deldare Ware. In 1922, Larkin advertised its Deldare Ware as a premium to its customers and shortly thereafter started importing Noritake china for premium purposes.

Noritake china in the Azalea, Savoy and Briarcliff patterns was offered in the 1924 Larkin catalog. In 1926, the Azalea pattern was shown in full color in the catalog, with many serving pieces available as premiums. Other Noritake patterns available in 1926 were Sheridan, with a multi-colored floral border, and also Scenic with a landscape scene. Noritake china, in certain patterns, was given in a premium plan which matched a dollar's worth of regular merchandise, purchased from the catalog, with a dollar's worth of china as a premium. The distribution of the premium goods was mostly throughout the eastern part of the United States because of the location of the Larkin Company.

These early pieces of Noritake china are being shown by many antiques stores and are gathered up quickly by collectors who appreciate the exquisite detail of the designs and the treasured craftsmanship of every piece.

These backstamps will be found on the Azalea pattern china: Maple Leaf, Blue Rising Sun, Green "M" Wreath (9), Red "M" Wreath (9), and the Red Azalea Sprig (17). All backstamps may be collected together to make a set of china. One backstamp does not command a higher price than another. In fact, in order to collect a large variety of serving pieces, it will be necessary to have an assortment of backstamps.

The Maple Leaf and the Blue Rising Sun backstamps were probably used by an affiliated china factory in Japan, that was under contract with the Noritake Company to produce the Azalea pattern. The Maple Leaf backstamp was used on many different types of china ware and the color of the backstamp was either green or blue. According to a Noritake Company executive, the green color of the Maple Leaf backstamp was used on first grade wares and the blue color on second grade. I believe the first grade wares were more ornate in shape or design and used more gold than the second grade wares. The Azalea pattern china with the Maple Leaf backstamp, that I have seen, carries the blue colored ink.

The Azalea pattern of dinnerware was produced by the Noritake Company until 1941.

The Price Guide is based on near mint condition pieces. Some pieces such as the shell bowl, covered candy dish, child's set, demitasse coffee pot, 16" platter, toothpick holder, and the round vase were made in limited quantities and will demand high prices.

Hand painted

MAPLE LEAF

First used in 1891 by the Morimura Brothers of Noritake. Color of ink was green for first grade and blue for second grade.

RISING SUN

Color ink used was blue.

Plate #7

Top row left: Azalea pattern dinnerware — 7½" plate
Backstamp: (9) green
Top row right: Sheridan pattern dinnerware — 9½" cake plate
Backstamp: (10) green
Bottom row: Azalea pattern dinnerware as shown in the Larkin Company catalog. (Photocopy permission of Red White and Blue Shop, Danbury, CN).

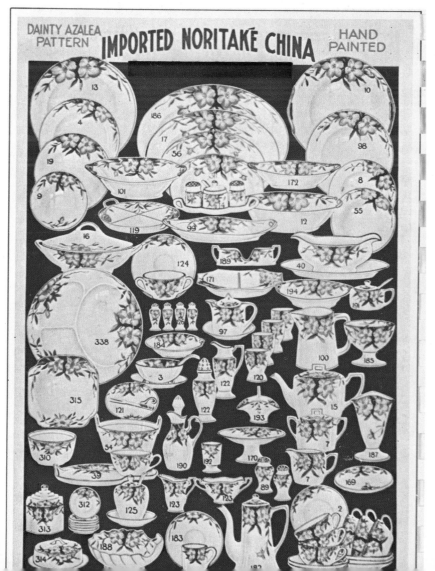

DAINTY AZALEA PATTERN — IMPORTED NORITAKE CHINA — HAND PAINTED

NORITAKE LUSTER

Noritake luster china was manufactured extensively from about 1921 to the middle 1930's. It was perhaps one of the most innovative looks to come from Japan. It stood out from all other china because of its brightly colored underglazes.

The luster glazing process was a form of decoration which used a thin metallic film over the basic glaze of the china. The colors used were gold, tan, red, orange, pearl, blue and green. The china, fired in a low reducing temperature kiln, produced an iridescent surface to the glaze and kept the egg-shell thin items from warping. In some cases, the artwork seemed rather hastily done, but the sheen of the colors catching the light was magnificent. Because of the period of history in which luster was manufactured, the handpainted decorations may represent anything from the Art Deco look to themes in nature of flowers or landscapes.

Generally, the shapes of the pieces were simple in line and were designed for specific uses. Sometimes, the piece of china was shaped like the food it contained. For example, lemon slices might be served on a plate shaped like a lemon slice. The great diversity of shapes and sizes included examples such as hatpin holders, jam jars, egg cups, hair receivers, napkin rings, mayonnaise bowls with spoon, nut bowls, vases, children's sets, cigarette holders, facepowder boxes, salt cellars and even spooners, which were used to stack spoons for a buffet table. The collector must often rely on his or her own judgment as to the importance of the shapes and designs of each piece of luster and the era it represents.

The three backstamps used on Noritake luster china are illustrated in the chapter on backstamps. Each used a different color of ink. The first, printed in green contained the letter "M" in the wreath with "Noritake" printed above it. It had "Handpainted" and "Made in Japan" printed below the wreath. The second backstamp, first used in the middle 1920's, was printed in red and was identical in design to the first. The third backstamp, in blue ink, had the spider design with "Noritake" written above and "Made in Japan" printed below it. This backstamp was registered in Japan in 1921 and was probably used until the late 1920's or early 1930's. So, by referring to the backstamp, it is possible to distinguish the period of time that a particular piece of luster china was produced.

From the collector's viewpoint, luster china produced by the Noritake Company is rather difficult to find. There is an abundance of the "Made in Japan" pieces in children's tea sets and other luncheon sets, but they do not have the Noritake backstamp. Considering that Noritake produced luster china for such a short time, it is understandable why it is not extensively known or more available. But with the current collectors' infatuations with Nippon wares, including early Noritake, can it be long before luster china will become more widely appreciated and collected?

Plate #8
Noritake-Luster

Top Row:

Jam Jar. Matching saucer and round shaped ladle. Cream colored luster with blown-out strawberries and leaves on front. Red finial handle. (9) green.

Bowl 2¼"x9". Gold luster border with typical cabin in a landscape of lake and trees. (9) green.

Jam Jar. Matching saucer and oval shaped ladle. Gold luster covers entire jar. Cover has blown-out purple grapes and green leaves. Brown handle. (9) green.

Middle Row:

Dish 4½"x7¼". Gold luster background with pink flowers on four sides and middle. (9) red.

Vase 6"x7¼". Item shown on cover. Twin-sided with brightly colored parrot sitting in middle. Blue luster finish with gold luster base and inside of vase. A very special piece. (9) green.

Bowl 6¾". Wide blue luster border. Center design is a Spanish Galleon vessel sailing on green and black water. Two pierced handles. (9) red.

Bottom Row:

Mayonnaise set. Three pieces. Green border with orange poppies and small blue flowers. Center is pearl luster. Round ladle. (9) red.

Bowl 7¼". Blue luster border with Art Deco-type design of flowers on a black background. Gold trimmed handles. (9) red.

Powder Puff Box. Gold luster background with a Victorian-type lady with lilac dress holding a large black ostrich fan. Souvenir of Standing Rock, Wisconsin Dells. (9) red.

Cigarette Holder. Gold luster with green trim. Decal of a brown horse on each side. (9) red.

Plate #9
Noritake-Luster

Top Row:

Plate 7¾". Blue luster border with a scene of mountains and hills in shades of purple with a lime green tree. (9) green.

Salt & Pepper. Individual set of salt cellar, pepper shaker and tray. Green luster background with Chinese lantern design. (10) green.

Bowl 7" round. Blue luster border with house by the lake scene. Gold trim on handles. (9) green.

Candy Dish. Gold border with landscape scene of house in the woods. Single handle. (9) red.

Middle Row:

Lemon Dish 5". Gold luster border. Center design is a lady dressed in lemon yellow and black feeding a parrot on a ring. (9) green.

Ash Tray — Individual. Blue luster with two colorful parrots on a perch. (9) green.

Salt Cellar — Individual. Gold luster inside with blue outside. (9) red.

Muffineer set. Creamer and powdered sugar shaker both have bright orange top and bottom. Design is a blue bird sitting on a branch with pink flowers on a pearl luster background. Gold top on shaker. (9) red.

Mayonnaise Bowl. Pink border with pearl luster on inside. Three gold ball feet. (9) green.

Bottom Row:

Bowl 6". Round with gold luster border and white center. Two floral designs in multi-colors. (9) red.

Demitasse Cups. Orange and green luster with gold trim. Center design is a pair of phoenix birds (11).

Bowl. Three-sided with orange border. Cabin by the lake scene. Three pierced handles. (9) red.

Plate #10
Noritake-Luster

Top Row:

Child's set. Two pieces with plate and cup. Design is a boy pushing a girl in carriage with dog in front. Blue luster border and trim. (9) red.

Compote. Gold and blue luster background with stylized pink and red flowers. Blue base and black handles. (9) green.

Plate 8". Gold border with white center. Eight-sided. Center design of flowers. (9) green.

Middle Row:

Bowl. Gold luster border with two flowers designs. Center is white. Three raised feet. (9) green.

Nut Bowl 7½" square. Blown-out walnuts on outside with raised basket weave design. Silver rope circles the edge and handles. Gold luster inside. Very well done. (9) green.

Bowl 5¼" round. Gold luster border with swans swimming in lake. Three balled feet. (9) red.

Bottom Row:

Cream and Sugar. Blue luster background with multi-colored flowers. Gold trim and handles and edge. White inside. (9) green.

Hair Receiver. Part of a dresser set. Blue luster with alternating red and green on border. Three raised feet. (9) red.

Tray 8½"x11". Orange luster background with stylized flowers and stripes. Art Deco look. Design is balanced each way it is turned. (9) red.

OKURA ART CHINA VASES

Okura china was first created in 1919 in the suburbs of Tokyo by Magobei Okura and his son, Kazuchika, who were also the founders of the Noritake Company. They were chiefly concerned about making the most beautiful and highest quality of china in the world. They concentrated their experiments on improving the materials and firing and were successful.

Okura china is made of highly refined material and is fired at exceptionally intense heat for extreme strength and durability. It is fine-grained, smooth and rich with exquisitely hand-decorated designs painted by native artisans. Because of its supreme beauty and quality, Okura china has long been commissioned by the Japanese Imperial families and by Japanese Embassies throughout the world.

Each piece of Okura china is individually produced. If you own a dinnerware set of Okura china and break a cup, you will have to send the saucer for the cup back to the company to insure proper alignment of the new cup to the saucer.

Okura china is scarce in the United States market, because of the limited production and the high price it demands. The backstamp these vases carry can be seen in the chapter on backstamps (backstamp number 37).

Plate #11

Top Row:
1. Pine
2. Golden Clematis
3. Golden Grape

Second Row:
1. Orchid
2. Blue Camellia
3. Golden Grape
4. Blue Rose
5. Golden Cattleya (Cobalt)

Third Row:
1. Clematis (Cobalt)
2. Blue Roses
3. Tiger Lily
4. Golden Oriental Flower

Fourth Row:
1. Golden Flower
2. Golden Rose
3. Paulownia
4. Cobalt Sarasa
5. Golden Grape

Bottom Row:
1. Peony
2. Blue Rose
3. Arabesque Rose
4. Camellia
5. Blue Rose

Photocopy courtesy of Noritake Company, Inc.

19A-1196 (H-11½")

29A-9026 (H-7½")

19A-9146 (H

2A-3431

12A-9431

12A-1276

12A-8011

12A-9086

47A-9371

47A-8011

60A-3361

60A-1356

20A-1286

20A-2016

20A-9126

20A-9441

20A-9076

49A-3081

49A-8011

49A-3131

15A-3051

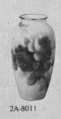
2A-8011

BONE CHINA FIGURINES

These bone china figurines show a unique warmth and jewel-like translucency because of the composition of the raw materials used in production. Basically, the chemical composition is a combination of fusible silicates of aluminum, such as petunse, china stone and feldspar, and nonfusible silicates of aluminum, such as kaolin and china clay. In addition to these ingredients, Noritake adds animal bone to the body. It is the animal bone, called calcined bone ash, that gives these figurines their special whiteness. These hard paste china figurines are still being made in Japan.

Figurine

Ayu (sweet fish) large or small

Bantam, male or female

Bull and boy — height, 180 mm

Bull and woman (God Zeus and Europa)

> This figurine represents the love story between the great God Zeus and Europa, the princess of Phoenicia. According to the myth, Zeus fell in love with the princess when he first saw her. In order to approach her, he changed himself into the form of a bull and then carried her away to Crete.

Crane — height, 280 mm
Crane and brood — height, 165mm
Crane, incubating
Deer and fawn
Dogs
Dog and puppy — height, 165mm
Eagle Catching Fish — height, 360 mm
Eagles — height, 370 mm
Family of Deer
Fowl, Long Tailed — height, 335mm
Fantail Bird, male or female
Geisha — height, 215mm
    The lovely, talented geisha has been associated
    with Japanese entertainment for many years. They
    represent the joy and luxury in Japan of yesterday.

Gold Fish, large or small
Golfer, Arnold Palmer 600 Club
Golfer, hitting — height, 310mm
Golfer, hitting — height, 260mm
Golfer, woman
Giraffes — height, 345 mm
Horse and Woman — height, 285mm
Horses, three — height, 260mm

Kan-non (The Goddess of Mercy) — height, 575mm
    In the Buddhist faith, Kan-non represents mercy
    and kindness. The tender and loving expression on
    the face of the image is said to mirror a mother's
    love for her child. And many mothers take their
    children to Kan-non to beg for health and hap-
    piness.
Kasaodori (Dance of Sado Province) — height,
225mm
    This kimono-clad maid with the kasa or head cover-
    ing represents colorful Japanese folk dancing.
Mandarin Duck, male or female
Mare and Foal — height, 165mm
Oharame (woman carrying sticks)
Penguin, male or female
Rabbit
Ranryooh (The Dance of the Dragon King)
    A lone dancer wearing a costume and a golden
    dragon mask, dances to the music of the court
    musicians. With a small stick, he displays his feel-
    ings in lively movements. This dance, which is sym-
    bolic of Shintoism, is part of Gagaku, the music of
    the Imperial Court.

Red Apple Bowl with cover
Reindeer — height, 380mm
Stag and Eagles — height, 675mm
Swan, male or female

Tennyo (The Angelic Nymphs)
Beautiful angels are said to inhabit the Buddhist heaven. These glorious creatures represent the highest form of created life in Japanese folklore.

Trout — height, 295mm
White Bear
Woman and Doves — height, 430mm

Yagibushi (Drum of Village Festival) — height, 195mm
Historically in Japan, the drum has been used to accompany the chants of the folk singers at village festivals. Years ago, the drum was a wooden bucket, and the drummer used sticks to beat on the sides and top. Gradually, the wooden bucket developed into the large decorated drums which add so much color to the village festivals even today.

Plate #12
Bone China Figurines

Top Row:

Reindeer
A majestic species of the antlered deer found in northern America, Europe and Asia.

Tennyo
These angels are gloriously attired creatures and represent the highest form of created life. Wearing their beautiful celestial robes, they fly among the heavens. Japanese folklore has many stories of these heavenly beings coming to earth to brighten the hearts of man.

Bottom Row:

Golfer — Man
A golfer playing his wood club on a long drive is a tribute to a game played in many countries.

Eagle Catching Fish
A beautiful bird showing its strength and keenness of vision in catching fish.

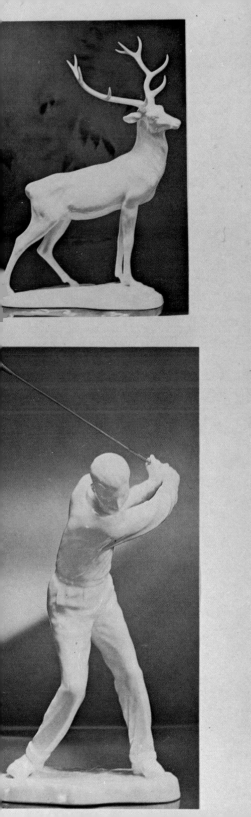

SHINSHA BONE CHINA
The Fiery Red of the Setting Sun

The fantastically bright Shinsha glaze was developed more than 600 years ago. The red color is so brilliant it is said that the artist used powder from ground rubies. It is also told that the artist shed his own blood if the red color did not meet his expectations. So, the color became known as the red of sacrifice. Shinsha is one of the most beautiful glazes perfected by the Noritake Company.

Shinsha vase productions were intended for both the Japanese market and for export. They are definitely an accurate reflection of the Japanese taste.

Prices will vary from under $100 to nearly $500. You may want to refer to the price guide for individual prices.

Plate #13
Shinsha Bone China

Top Row:
1. Red vase with roses — height, 9½"
2. Red vase with roses — height, 12"
3. Red vase with roses — height, 14½"

Bottom Row:
1. Red vase with ridges — height, 9½"
2. Red vase with flowers — height, 12"
3. Red plain vase — height, 14½"

BONE CHINA VASES

Bone china is the finest in an ultra-thin body with translucency and a perfect glaze. The calcined bone ash added to this body gives it a special whiteness which lends itself to a large variety of beautiful designs.

These vases rely on the original artists' work and are carefully reproduced with gypsum molds to preserve their character and beauty. Each vase is individual and carries muted colors in restrained and tasteful decorations. The decorations are usually asymmetrical, having different designs on each side of the vase. A bone china vase with a bouquet of roses on the front will probably have a single rose on the backside. Or, a vase with a landscape design will show different parts of the landscape around the vase.

Remember that a piece of china is not bone china unless it is so marked on the backstamp. Bone china is becoming very scarce because of the high cost of production.

Following is a list of some of the bone china vases produced by Noritake. The number in parentheses refers to the backstamp of each vase. You may wish to refer to the corresponding number in the chapter on backstamps.

Description	Height	Backstamp
Dragon — grey and white	9½"	(29)
Poppies — salmon color	5½"	(29)
Roses — pink	8½"	(29)
Roses — yellow and pink	6½"	(57)
Scenery — Landscape — yellow sides	9½"	(29)
Scenery — Landscape of Japan	9"	(57)
Scenery — Landscape — brown tones	6½"	(29)

Please refer to the price guide for values on the above vases.

Plate #14
Bone China Vases
Top Row:
Landscape of countryside, Roses — pink.

Middle Row:
Poppies, salmon colored.

Bottom Row:
Landscape, house on cliff, Roses — yellow and pink.

LIMITED EDITIONS

Decorative limited editions have become a collecting phenomenon. Millions of people are buying limited editions as a hobby. Most collectors are interested in these editions for aesthetic reasons, with hope of eventually realizing a profit, too. This hobby has become the third most popular collectors' item, outranked only by coins and miniatures.

Noritake Co., Inc. produced its first limited edition in 1971 in the shape of an Easter egg made of bone china. While Easter passes unobserved by Oriental cultures, the beliefs relating to the egg add color to today's Easter customs. In Japan, eggs are elaborately painted and the more beautiful the egg, the more respect and honor are bestowed on the owner.

EASTER EGGS	Original retail selling price	Quantity made
1971 (First Issue) "Bunnies"	$10.00	21,000
1972 "Easter Lilies"	$10.00	21,000
1973 "Hen & Chicks"	$10.00	22,800
1974 "Easter Basket"	$11.00	22,000
1975 "Mallard Ducks"	$14.50	22,050
1976 "Girl's Bonnet"	$15.00	22,050

1977 "Spring Lambs"	$15.00	15,000
1978 "Spring Blossoms"	$17.50	15,000
1979 "Bird"	$20.00	

In 1972, Noritake produced the first limited edition of the bone china Christmas bell to ring in the holiday season. The second Christmas bell began the designs based upon the famed Christmas carol, "The Twelve Days of Christmas".

CHRISTMAS BELL	Original retail selling price	Quantity made
1972 (First Issue) "Holly"	$14.50	28,000
1973 "Partridge"	$15.00	18,200
1974 "Turtle Doves"	$16.00	10,000
1975 "French Hens"	$18.00	10,000
1976 "Collie Birds"	$18.00	10,000
1977 "Golden Rings"	$20.00	10,000
1978 "Geese A-Laying"	$25.00	8,600

In 1973, Noritake crafted the bone china heart for Valentine's Day. These hearts reflect the universal spirit of love and affection.

VALENTINE HEART	Original retail selling price	Quantity made
1973 (First Issue)		
"Boy & Dove"	$14.50	10,300
1974 "Boy and Girl"	$14.50	5,000
1975 "Angel"	$14.50	5,000
1976 "Ribbons"	$14.50	2,000
1977 "Will You Be Mine"	$17.50	1,000
1978 "Butterflies & Flowers"	$20.00	1,000
1979 "Birds Kissing"	$22.00	?

In the early 1970s, Noritake produced the first issues of the old fashion Mother's Day and Father's Day mugs. Production of both of these mugs has since been discontinued.

MOTHER'S DAY OLD FASHION	Original retail selling price	Quantity made
1973 (First Issue) "Birds"	$15.00	6,000
1974 "Yellow Flowers"	$17.00	6,000
1975 "Pink Carnations"	$17.00	1,300
1976 "Blue & Yellow Flower"	$20.00	400

FATHER'S DAY
OLD FASHION

1972 (First Issue) "Rope"	$18.00	10,000
1973 "Leaves"	$18.00	9,000
1974 "Men"	$17.00	2,500
1975 "Court Cards"	$18.00	1,000
1976 "Fish-Trout"	$20.00	400

Noritake issued in 1974 the first bone china figurines depicting motherhood in the animal kingdom, for Mother's Day.

MOTHER'S DAY FIGURINE	Original retail selling price	Quantity made
1974 (First Issue)		
"Doe & Fawn"	$50.00	2,800
1975 "Quarter Horse"	$50.00	2,800
1976 "Cat & Kitten"	$55.00	2,800
1977 "Irish Setter"	$55.00	2,500

SPORTS

Tennis Cup "Man Playing Tennis"	1,000
Arnold Palmer "600 Club" Golfer	600

Plate #15
Limited Editions

Top Row:
  Father's Day Old Fashion Mug, 1972
  Father's Day Old Fashion Mug, 1975
  Mother's Day Old Fashion Mug, 1975

Middle Row:
  Mother's Day Figurine, 1976
  Arnold Palmer Golfer

Bottom Row:
  Christmas Bell, 1975
  Christmas Bell, 1976
  Valentine Heart, 1976
  Easter Egg, 1975
  Easter Egg, 1976

Plate #16

NORITAKE DINNERWARE

This 92 piece set of dinnerware pattern "Caroline-6671" was purchased in San Francisco, California, in 1967. The design of Caroline has two bands of platinum separated by a richly detailed leaf scroll composed entirely of platinum and raised white decoration.

In 1972, this pattern of Caroline dinnerware was discontinued from production. It is not stocked in the United States and is no longer available in matching replacement pieces. Discontinued patterns of dinnerware belong to the past and their availability is uncertain.

You may wish to refer to the chapter Noritake Dinnerware Patterns pages 91-105, for a listing of discontinued patterns and how to acquire matching replacement pieces.

NORITAKE BACKSTAMPS

A number of theories have been formulated on the colors used in different Noritake backstamps in order to arrive at an exact date of usage. At this time, it is impossible for several different reasons to determine by the backstamp or the color of ink used the exact date a ware was produced. One reason is that Noritake used several different backstamps during any given period and they overlap each other. Also, the very early records were written in old Japanese, which differs from the Japanese used today. Maybe, in the future someone will translate the old Japanese writings into English and we will have some of the answers regarding dates, colors and location of production. Another reason is that some of the records were destroyed and are not available.

The factual recorded information we have is that most backstamps used by Noritake were registered in Japan and/or with the United States Patent Office. These records state when a particular backstamp was first used. This first-used date should help to designate a period of time in which a ware carrying a particular backstamp was produced.

The following backstamps used by Noritake are intended only as a guide to collectors. The Noritake backstamp appears on the underside of a ware and is always under the glaze.

1 "M" IN WREATH—NIPPON

Backstamp was registered in Japan in 1911 but was probably used much earlier. The "M" stands for the Morimura family. The inks used were blue, green and magenta. The items with the blue backstamp appear to be older in design than the green or magenta backstamp.

2 RC NIPPON

Backstamp was registered in Japan in 1911. RC stood for Royal Ceramic. "Hand Painted" is in red ink and "RC Nippon" is in green ink. Very high quality china with intricate gold work.

3 NIPPON—HAND PAINTED

Spider symbol is the crest of the Morimura family. Backstamp was used in the very early years of Noritake. The ink used was blue.

4 RC NORITAKE & NIPPON

Backstamp used in the early years of Noritake. The ink used was green. RC stood for Royal Ceramic. Pure white china with lavish use of gold.

5 NORITAKE—NIPPON

Used on blanks that were decorated outside of Japan. Ink was green.

6 NORITAKE "M" IN WREATH

Used for a short period of time between 1914-1921. Ink used was green. Used on dinnerware. Compare with (9) which is similar but uses "Made in Japan" under wreath.

7 NORITAKE—NIPPON

Used before 1921, mainly on dinner-ware. Ink used was deep red. Registered in Japan in 1906 for the domestic market.

8 RC NORITAKE

Backstamp was registered in Japan in 1908.

9 NORITAKE—HAND-PAINTED—MADE IN JAPAN

Backstamp will be found in red and green ink. The green ink is the older backstamp and was changed to red in approx. 1925.

10 NORITAKE— MADE IN JAPAN

Inks used were red and green. Backstamp will be found on the old dinnerware pattern Sheridan, produced in 1926. Some backstamps will contain the words "U.S. Design Pat. Applied For". Registered in Japan in 1921 and in India in 1926.

11 NORITAKE— MADE IN JAPAN

Backstamp was registered in Japan in 1912. Spider design is the crest of the Morimura family which stood for the protection of the people. Ink used was blue. Backstamp used on the Phoenix Bird "HoWo" pattern of dinnerware. Registered in London, England in 1908.

12 NORITAKE

Backstamp was registered in Japan in 1930. Used on the "White and Gold" pattern of dinnerware.

13 NORITAKE

Backstamp was registered in Japan in 1931.

14 NORITAKE "M"

Backstamp was registered in Japan in 1933.

15 NORITAKE CHINA "M"

Backstamp was registered in Japan in 1933. Don't confuse with the "N" backstamp below which was registered 20 years later. Registered U.S. Patent Office in July 11, 1950, Filed Mar. 25, 1948, claims use since Jan. 1, 1933. Blue wreath with gold center and ribbon.

JAPAN

16 NORITAKE CHINA "N"

Backstamp was registered in Japan in 1953. Blue wreath with gold colored background on "N" and ribbon. Black letters.

AZALEA PATT.

HANDPAINTED

JAPAN

NO. 19322
252622

17 NORITAKE—
AZALEA PATTERN

Backstamp was registered in Japan in 1934. The Azalea pattern was given as a premium by the Larkin Co. Production of the pattern was discontinued in 1941. Azalea is one of the most sought-after patterns by collectors. The last of four backstamps used on Azalea patterned china. Red ink.

18 NORITAKE CHINA

Backstamp was registered in Japan in 1934.

NITORITE

19 NORITAKE NITORITE
Backstamp was registered in Japan in 1939.

NITOROX

20 NORITAKE NITOROX
Backstamp was registered in Japan in 1939.

21 NORITAKE BONE CHINA
Backstamp registered in Japan in 1940. The symbol is a Japanese character for a spider.

22 NORITAKE NTK BONE CHINA

Backstamp was registered in Japan in 1940. N.T.K. stands for Nippon Toki Kaisha.

23 NORITAKE "M"

Backstamp was registered in Japan in 1940. "M" stands for the Morimura family.

24 NORITAKE "M"

Green wreath with brown M and tan ribbon and crown.

25 NORITAKE—HAND PAINTED

Backstamp was registered in Japan in 1940.

26 NORITAKE—ROYALE BONE CHINA

Hand painted. Backstamp was registered in Japan in 1941.

27 NORITAKE—NIPPON TOKI KAISHA

Backstamp was registered in Japan in 1949.

28 NORITAKE— MADE IN JAPAN

Backstamp was registered in Japan in 1949. Compare with similar backstamp, number 11, registered in 1911.

NIPPON TOKI KAISHA
JAPAN

29 NORITAKE—BONE CHINA

Backstamp was registered in Japan in 1949. Used on vases. Leaves are green and tureen is tan. Printed letters are red with Noritake in gold.

MADE IN
OCCUPIED JAPAN

30 NORITAKE—MADE IN OCCUPIED JAPAN

Backstamp was registered in Japan in 1949. Japan was occupied from Sept. 1945 to April 1952 by the Allied Forces. Colors blue and gold.

MADE IN
OCCUPIED JAPAN

31 NORITAKE—MADE IN OCCUPIED JAPAN

Backstamp was registered in Japan in 1949. First used in 1947 and used for only six months.

JAPAN

32 NORITAKE—ROSE CHINA

Backstamp was registered in Japan in 1949. Made after WWII and exported under the Rose China backstamp. Not high quality.

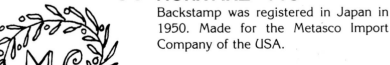

33 NORITAKE—MC

Backstamp was registered in Japan in 1950. Made for the Metasco Import Company of the USA.

34 NORITAKE—RC
Backstamp was registered in Japan in 1950.

35 NORITAKE—RC
Backstamp was registered in Japan in 1950.

36 NORITAKE—IC
Backstamp was registered in Japan in 1950.

37 NORITAKE—OKURA

JAPAN

Okura art china was first created in 1919. It has been commissioned by the Japanese Imperial families. The factory was started by Baron Okura as a hobby. All designs are done by hand.

38 NORITAKE—IVORY

Backstamp was registered in Japan in 1950.

39 NORITAKE—NITTO WARE

Backstamp was registered in Japan in 1950.

40 NORITAKE

Backstamp was registered in Japan in 1951. Compare the shape of the "r" with current Noritake logo, as shown in number 50.

Noritake

41 NORITAKE

Backstamp was registered in Japan in 1951.

Noritake China

42 NORITAKE

Backstamp was registered by the Noritake Company in Japan in 1951.

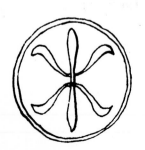

43 NORITAKE— ALBION CHINA
Backstamp was registered in Japan in 1952.

44 NORITAKE—NITTO WARE
Backstamp was registered in Japan in 1952.

45 NORITAKE
Backstamp was registered in Japan in 1952.

46 NORITAKE—BONE CHINA

Backstamp was registered in Japan in 1953.

47 NORITAKE CHINA

Backstamp was registered in Japan in 1953.

48 NORITAKE

Backstamp was registered in Japan in 1953.

49 NORITAKE—RC

Registered U.S. Patent Sept. 9, 1967, Filed May 16, 1966, First used Jan. 1, 1947. The lining in the mark does not indicate a particular color. Used on Chinaware.

50 NORITAKE

Registered in U.S. Patent Office on July 11, 1950, Filed Mar. 25, 1948, First used on Jan. 1, 1948 for dinnerware made of china. Registered in Japan in 1955.

51 NORITAKE

Registered in U.S. Patent Office on July 11, 1950. First used in October 1949 on dinnerware made of china.

52 NORITAKE IVORY CHINA

Backstamp was registered in U.S. in 1973. The words "Ivory China" are disclaimed apart from mark as shown. First used in Oct. 1964 on tableware and dinnerware.

53 NORITAKE—BONE CHINA

Backstamp registered with U.S. Patent Office in Nov. 1973. The words "Bone China" apart from mark as shown. First used in commerce in Jan. 1953. Used on dinnerware and tableware.

54 NEW NORITAKE

Registered in Japan in 1954.

New Noritake

55 NORITAKE

Backstamp was registered in Japan in 1955.

56 NORITAKE—IVORY CHINA

Registered in Japan in 1965. Used on the Artcraft China Collection of table accessories. First used in commerce Nov. 1964.

57 NORITAKE—BONE CHINA

Backstamp used on vases and other bone china wares. Design done in gold with black outlines on leaves and tureen. Compare with backstamp number 29.

From 1878 to 1884, the Morimura brothers of Noritake had their own decoration kiln in Japan. The backstamps they used are unknown. Then, from 1884 to 1890, they had affiliated decorating factories all over Japan. The backstamps were in Chinese characters and told the country of origin.

Samples are not shown, but the following backstamps were used by the Noritake Company on wares for the domestic market in Japan.
Royal Satsuma
Royal Kaita
Royal Sometuka
Royal Nichiki
Royal Kinran

GLOSSARY

BLOWN-OUT

Blown-out describes a piece of china that has the shape of an object, such as a nut or fruit, extending beyond the exterior or interior surfaces. The blown-out area is achieved by pushing out the design on one side of the dish and leaving the other side hollow. Early wares favored shapes of the chestnut, almond, walnut and brazil nuts, plus animals and Indians. Later wares used grapes, strawberries and other fruits to extend the design in a three-dimensional effect. Blown-out wares are scarce and are truly collector items.

CORALENE BEADING

The raised beading found on the very early Noritake wares was formed by adding tiny dots of clay to the surface. This painstaking task was done while the ware was in the biscuit state, which had been fired once. Thus, the beading design became part of the ware. Then, the beading was colored, usually in gold, to make it look like small jewels. Later wares used an imitation coralene beading from dots of enamel without the clay dots underneath.

ENAMEL

Enamel was a kind of opaque glass, often brilliantly colored, used as a decorative coating for china ware.

JAPANESE CORALENE

This method of decorating, usually on glass, used tiny glass beads which were fired to the base ware. The result was a shiny, almost jewel-like, decoration. This method of decorating was customarily used on satin glass, which Noritake did not produce.

MORIAGA

Moriaga is the Japanese term for any type of raised clay or enamel decoration on wares, which includes slip-trailing and coralene beading. It is the term most often used to describe large, decorative pieces of clay that form the design. Only the early Noritake wares used the moriaga techniques, which can be very elaborate.

RELIEF

This term describes the elevation or projection of a design from a flat surface. It is also used to describe the total ware that is produced using this method of decoration.

SLIP-TRAILING

Slip-trailing is a type of decoration that uses liquid clay called slip to create a raised ridge design. Slip was applied to the dry ware with a tube and trailed on the ware to serve as a raised outline or border for the design. One Japanese method used grey slip to form the three-clawed Japanese dragon on vases and other wares.

WEDGWOOD-NIPPON

This describes the Japanese blue and white wares resembling those made by the Wedgwood Company in England. These wares are unglazed vitreous fine stoneware stained blue to provide suitable background for the white classical relief designs. The relief designs were made by pressing clay into a mold and then applying the design by hand to the clay ware. These wares are very rare and demand high prices.

NORITAKE DINNERWARE PATTERNS

Since Noritake's founding, thousands of dinnerware patterns have been produced. One pattern named "White and Gold" has been produced since the 1930's. A dinnerware pattern is produced until sales decline, and then it is phased out of production over a three-year period.

Nearly all Noritake dinnerware is identifiable by the name and number found on the back of the dinner plate. Very early dinnerware patterns were not numbered or named, but their age can be determined by the backstamp on the back of the dinner plate. Every Noritake dinnerware set has a backstamp.

Many people are finding that they can purchase an older dinnerware set at a lower price than a new set. Consequently, many estate shops and antiques dealers are showing complete dinnerware sets for sale. Prices vary, as some patterns are in more demand than others. Generally, the early, more ornate dinnerware patterns have a higher value than the plainly decorated patterns.

It can be frustrating trying to replace a missing cup or plate if you already possess a set of Noritake dinnerware. But, there is hope for finding a replacement piece. Several firms specialize in matching old Noritake patterns. These matching services buy and sell discontinued dinnerware patterns. You must send them a card listing the pattern name and number, and the pieces wanted for replacement. The service will either reply that they have the pieces, or they will file the card until those pieces are available. Writing to several·services will increase your chances of finding the replacement piece. You can find the addresses of these matching services by paging through antiques newspapers at your local library or bookstore. Also, Noritake today produces two shapes of cups and saucers, with either a silver or gold band, to match old dinnerware sets. These cups and saucers are available through any dealer selling Noritake China.

The following Noritake dinnerware patterns have been discontinued. Each pattern is listed by name and number, which is on the back of each plate, and the year it was discontinued. A pattern discontinued before 1949 may not appear in this list, as those records are not available.

Pattern-Number	Year	Pattern-Number	Year
Aberdeen-6727	1972	Allston-6304	1974
Adala-5273	1960	Almont-6125	1967
Adele-5126	Disc.	Alrea-	Disc
Adrienne-5143	1956	Amherst-501	1953
Aida-2043	1975	Amorette-6356	1968
Aileen-5525	Disc.	Amywood-5154	1956
Alameda-520	1958	Andover-5654	1960
Alberta-5806	1963	Audrea-5524	1962
Aldea-3083	1954	Anemone-5011	Disc
Alden-5036	1952	Angela-506	1953
Aldive-	Disc.	Angela BE-6378	1968
Alhambra-5157	Disc.	Angela GR-6375	1968
Alice-5267	1960	Angela TA-6377	1968
Alicia-5762	1965	Anita-757	1968
Allenby-6302	1968	Anjou-6408	1967
Allison-5313	1958	Annette-5264	1955

Pattern-Number	Year	Pattern-Number	Year
Annulaire-6689	1970	Azalea-19322	Disc.
April-B111	1968	Azalea-252622	Disc.
Arcadia-5165	1953	Babette-593	1967
Arcola-5149	1954	Balboa-6123	1972
Arden-5603	1963	Bambina-5791	1968
Ardine-5176	1951	Bamburg-5942	1966
Ardis-5772	1967	Barbara-6009	1966
Ardmore-3066	1952	Barbizon-6523	1970
Argyle-5311	1958	Barcarolle-6655	1972
Ariana-6358	1966	Barcelona-6673	1973
Arielle-5801	1962	Barclay-6028	Disc.
Arlene-5802	1967	Baroda-5125	1953
Arlington-5221	1960	Barossa-9011	1975
Armand-6315	1970	Barton-6305	1971
Arroyd-6318	1967	Basilica-6957	1974
Arunta-9007	1975	Beaumont-5775	Disc.
Ashby-6201	1965	Beaumont-5796	1961
Ashley-5653	1960	Bedford-5761	Disc.
Astor-6321	1967	Beguine-2033	1975
Astor Rose-6515	1974	Belda-6342	1972
Astoria-5171	1954	Belinda-5093	1955
Astrid-5403	Disc.	Bella-5266	1955
Athena-6221	1966	Bellaire-5427	1957
Atwood-6026	1963	Bellemead-6314	1974
Auburn-5303	1955	Bellerose-8104	1964
Auburn-6733	1972	Bellfleur-6105	1967
Audrey-3078	1959	Belmont-5609	1967
Augusta-2025	1975	Benita-751	1974
Augustan-4987	1952	Benton-6204	1966
Aurora-6955	1960	Berkeley-5784	1961
Automne-5626	1967	Bernice-5114	1953
Autumglory-6323	1967	Berrytime-6374	1968
Autumn-5534	1959	Berwick-5043	1952
Autumn Rose-2007	1974	Berwyn-5901	1962
Avalon-5150	1956	Beryl-4973	1950
Avon-5531	1960	Bessie-5788	1972
Ayudthaya-798	1975	Beverly-5162	1954
Azalea-5148	1952	Biarritz-6006	1974

Pattern-Number	Year	Pattern-Number	Yea
Black Coral-8701	Disc.	Brunswick-5410	196
Blair Rose-6519	1971	Bryce-5608	196
Blakesley-7554	1974	Callagold-5098	195.
Blanca-7545	1971	Calvert-5778	196
Bliss-5288	1955	Cambria-5217	Disc
Bloomfield-6042	1968	Camden-6350	197(
Bluaster-5006	1952	Camelot-3031	195.
Blue Bouquet-6735	1972	Cameo-4909	195.
Blue Garland-584/001	1969	Camille-6016	196.
Blue Rhapsody-B119	1972	Camillia-4735	195.
Blue Ribbon-770	1974	Candice-5509	196
Blue Rose-6005	Disc.	Canterbury-5226	196.
Bluebell-5558	1972	Canton-5027	196!
Bluecourt-6844	1973	Capri-5551	195!
Bluedale-5533	1961	Capri-7505	Disc
Bluedawn-4715	1952	Caprice-5933	197.
Bluelace-3032	1953	Cardinal-4731	195.
Bluemere-6457	1968	Carillon-6110	196.
Blueridge-5658	1970	Carla-508	Disc
Bluetone-6379	1970	Carleton-5034	195.
Bluetta-5898	1962	Carlisle-5544	196(
Bolero-2036	1975	Carlita-592	196!
Bonnibelle-5286	1955	Carlole-5402	196
Bordeaux-5496	1964	Carman-753	197!
Botan-5853	1962	Carmela-4732	195.
Boulogne-6788	1971	Carmelita-5223	Disc
Bouquet-2172	1972	Carnelian-8751	Disc
Bradford-5182	1961	Carol-607	196!
Brandon-6222	1970	Caroline-6671	197.
Breeze-2032	1975	Carolyn-3055	195.
Brenda-3064	1955	Cascade-5321	1958
Brentwood-5117	1953	Castille-2107	197!
Brewster-5645	1960	Cathay-763	197)
Briarcliff-	Disc.	Cathay-6029	1964
Brighton-7515	Disc.	Cavalier-6104	1968
Brilliant-761	1970	Cavatina-3028	195.
Bristol-5504	1963	Cecily-5766	196)
Brooklane-6112	1972	Celeste-5070	1953

94

Pattern-Number	Year	Pattern-Number	Year
Celeste-6804	1972	Clinton-6959	1960
Cerulean-4726	1953	Closter-6876	1973
Chadwick-6786	1971	Cloverdale-5552	1959
Chalice-6953	1974	Clovis-5855	1962
Champs-Elysees-6789	1972	Cobina-5432	1959
Chantell-7534	1969	Colby-5032	1954
Chantilly-792	1974	Collette-629	1970
Chantilly-5643	1960	Colmar-6419	1968
Charlene-5306	1955	Colonade-6111	Disc.
Charleroi-6907	Disc.	Colony-5932	1975
Charlotte-6606	1972	Colton-3081	1957
Charmaine-5506	1963	Columbia-6373	1968
Charmaine-6781	1973	Columbia W/Bl.-6386	1968
Chartres-5920	1963	Columbine-4917	1952
Chatham-5502	1965	Compton-6524	1971
Chatillon-5144	1954	Concetta-6414	1968
Chatsworth-5044	1954	Concord-4915	1952
Chaumont-6008	1968	Concord-6207	1968
Cheisea-5822	1963	Constance-5213	1958
Cheri-6352	1971	Constellation-7559	1974
Cherita-4787	1953	Contessa-2103	1975
Cheryl-5917	1960	Conway-5218	1954
Chinapeony-3060	1953	Corday-6120	1964
Chintz-3051	1953	Cordell-5408	1960
Cho-Cho-San-6936	1964	Cordova-5215	1956
Cho-Cho-San-6952	1959	Corinna-7535	1969
Christine-5111	1954	Corinne-5644	1960
Christine-5156	Disc.	Corinth-5503	1960
Cimarron-6308	1967	Corliss-5765	1963
Citrine-8753	Disc.	Cornwall-6307	1967
Claire-5902	1963	Corona-6502	1973
Clarabell-5557	1960	Coronado-6114	1964
Claremont-5214	1954	Coronet-6972	1964
Claridge-6020	1964	Corsage-5820	1962
Classic-5922	Disc.	Cortez-8752	Disc.
Classique-6807	1973	Cortina-7512	Disc.
Clayton-502	1953	Country Side-6899	1974
Clermont-5219	1954	Cranbrook-5785	1961

95

Pattern-Number	Year	Pattern-Number	Year
Elmhurst-5202	1956	Florence-5528	1961
Elsinore-5314	1955	Florette-423	1975
Embassy-6380	1970	Floria-7528	1968
Emerald-7560	1973	Floris-5088	1955
Encino-5315	1955	Fontana-5580	1959
Encore-5925	1967	Fortuna-6714	1971
Enid-6306	Disc.	Francine-5777	1961
Ensley-6958	1960	Gacahad-4783	Disc.
Esmeralda-5899	1964	Gail-6710	1972
Esprit-6959	1974	Gala-794	1974
Esquire-5404	1961	Galahad-4980	1951
Esteem	Disc.	Galaxy-6527	1975
Estelle-5542	Disc.	Gardena-3056	1956
Estrellita-6686	1971	Garland-5906	1963
Eunice-6508	Disc.	Garnet Rose-6512	1970
Eveningrose-6442	Disc.	Garvin-3039	1954
Fairfax-5451	Disc.	Gavott-B114	1968
Fairfield-6101	1964	Gayle-201	1971
Fantasia-7532	1973	Gayle-4972	1950
Farnsworth-5225	1954	Gaylord-5526	1967
Faye-6874	1973	Gaynor-B116	1967
Felicity-2001	1974	Geranium-4974	1952
Fern-5010	1952	Gina-6504	1972
Ferncliff-5779	1963	Glenbrook-5318	1957
Fernwood-5444	1959	Glencoe-6505	1974
Figaro-2042	1975	Glendale-5038	1954
Firenze-6674	1974	Glendon-5423	1962
Flanders-7514	Disc.	Glenfield-7515	1964
Flarella-4725	1952	Glenleaf-6660	1972
Fleur-2106	1975	Glennis-5804	1963
Fleurette-5909	1963	Glenrose-5206	1958
Fleurgold	Disc.	Glenview-6401	1968
Flomar-4723	1949	Glenville-6202	1965
Flomar-4918	1953	Gloria-6526	1975
Flora Valley-6958	1974	Glorianna-7526	1964
Floral Ring-8765	1975	Gold Fleur-6801	1972
Floralee-5151	1952	Goldana-4789	1953
		Goldart-5290	1963

Pattern-Number	Year	Pattern-Number	Yea
Goldawn-5581	1963	Greencrest-5641	195
Goldbeam-4786	1951	Greenfield-6585	196
Goldcoast-5897	1967	Greenlane-6023	196
Goldcourt-6843	1973	Greenmere-6458	196
Goldcroft-4983	1956	Greentone-6383	197
Goldenrose-5155	1952	Greenwood-5769	196
Goldette-5819	1962	Grenada-5911	196
Goldivy-7531	1970	Grenoble-6027	196
Goldkin-4985	1959	Greta-5272	196
Goldlane-5084	1970	Guenevere-6517	197
Goldlea-4793	Disc.	Guilford-5291	197
Goldmond-6132	1967	Gwendolyn-5083	195
Goldstone-5595	1965	Gwynne-5621	196
Goldthorn-6955	1973	Harcourt-6857	197
Goldvine-6444	1972	Harebell-5014	195
Goldwyn-6244	1972	Harley-6420	197
Gotham-6119	1967	Harmony-4712	195
Grace-6607	1970	Hartford-5944	196
Gracelyn-5856	1975	Hartsdale-6372	196
Gracewood-4984	1952	Hartsdale-6385	196
Gracia-5792	1961	Harvard Rose-6668	197
Gramacy-512	1954	Harvester-5562	196
Granada-3063	1954	Harveston-7524	196
Grandeur-5636	1960	Harwood-6312	197
Granville-5607	1962	Hawthorne-4914	195
Grayburn-5323	1963	Heidi-2156	Dis
Graycliff-5861	1964	Heiress Jade-6886	197
Graycrest-5824	1962	Heiress Ruby-6888	197
Graymere-6456	1972	Helene-5602	196
Graymont-6217	1966	Hermitage-6226	197
Grayoak-5646	Disc.	Holbrook-5635	196
Grayson-5697	1962	Hollis-5501	Dis
Graytone-6257	1973	Hometown-2153	197
Graywood-6041	1972	Horizon-6439	197
Green Bay-5353	1961	Huntley-5446	195
Green Coral-8702	Disc.	Hyannis-6535	196
Greenbriar-6802	1972	Hyde Park-6720	197
Greencourt-5322	1962	Ingrid-5904	196

Pattern-Number	Year	Pattern-Number	Year
Inverness-6716	1975	Kingston-6122	1965
Irmina-6601	1970	Kristin-6542	1971
Isadora-2059	1975	Krungtape-417	1974
Ivolily-4960	1952	L'Amor-6682	1973
Ivonne-7522	1974	Laguna-5159	1954
Ivyne-6605	1972	Lamarre-6859	1975
Jacqueline-6670	1973	Lamonia-5943	Disc.
Jana-6734	1972	Lancelot-6536	1970
Janette-6604	1973	Langdon-5164	1952
Jania-5631	1961	Laraine-4977	1953
Janice-5814	1962	LaSalle-5142	1956
Janine-5905	Disc.	Laura-5089	1955
Jardine-6208	1966	Laurel-5903	1970
Jaris-5604	1961	Laurette-5047	1958
Jean-6724	1972	Laverne-5810	1967
Jessie-7529	1968	Laveta-513	1955
Jewel-5443	1955	Leanna-6424	1968
Jonelle-6019	Disc.	Lehigh-6718	1971
Josephine-6240	1965	Lenore-517	Disc.
Josette-6543	1973	Leonie-5896	1968
Joy-227	1965	Leonore-6676	1974
Joyce-5174	1954	Leslie-6004	1966
Juanita-606	1972	Lexington-6435	1972
Judy-626	1968	Lila-6506	1973
Julie-5278	1955	Lillian-6662	1972
Juliet-6529	1970	Lilybell-5556	1964
June-6448	1968	Lima-9013	1973
Justine-6806	1974	Linda-507	1956
Karen-5141	1954	Linden-98217	Disc.
Karena-642	1969	Lindley-6954	1960
Kathleen-6722	1973	Lindrose-5234	1960
Kenilworth-2026	1975	Lindsay-6106	1965
Kensington-2029	1975	Linfield-B112	1968
Kent-5422	1963	Lise-6902	1974
Kenwood-5122	1953	Lisette-5773	1963
Kenwood-5222	Disc.	Lorelle-5914	1962
Kenyon-5262	1955	Lorene-5764	1965
Kerrie-6681	1970		

Pattern-Number	Year	Pattern-Number	Year
Lorenzo-6351	1970	Mavis-5543	1970
Lorraine-5320	1956	Maxine-641	1975
Lorraine-6785	1974	May-6661	1971
Louise-5204	1957	Maya-6213	1973
Lovell-6721	Disc.	Mayfair-6109	1972
Lozinia-9014	1973	Mayfield-4788	1953
Lucerne-5161	1953	Maysville-B106	1962
Lucerne-7508	Disc.	Meadow-8706	Disc.
Lucia-6452	1968	Medeci-5002	1953
Lucille-5813	1970	Melanie-B113	1971
Luise-5763	1963	Melanie-6381	1968
Lynbrook-4724	1953	Melissa-2104	1975
Lyndon-6116	1964	Melita-6205	1966
Lynne-5523	1961	Melrose-7518	1964
Lynwood-5307	1959	Melrose-6002	1972
Lyric-519	1955	Mentone-6018	1964
Mabel-6357	1970	Meredith-5918	1963
Madera-5106	1958	Merida-515	1955
Madiera-2056	1974	Meringo	Disc.
Maitland-5287	1955	Mesa-6370	1971
Malaya-7503	Disc.	Mesa-6382	1968
Maple Leaf-595	1969	Messina-4717	1953
Maplering-7530	1966	Michelle-6021	1964
Maplewood-B109	1971	Midori-6113	1967
Marcelle-619	1971	Mignon-6652	1970
Margaret-6243	1974	Mimi-6309	1967
Margarita-5049	1956	Minuet-6470	1971
Margot-5605	1968	Miramar-5452	1955
Maria-6675	1971	Miranda-6451	1968
Marietta-6653	1974	Miyako-7566	1974
Marilyn-6654	Disc.	Mizuadi-4976	Disc.
Marion-6951	1974	Moderne-5921	1963
Mariposa-6411	1967	Monaco-6725	1971
Marlene-6015	1963	Moneta-5050	1953
Marquis-7540	1974	Monica-5817	1963
Marsha-516	1955	Monnette	Disc.
Martha-6344	1968	Montage-8764	1975
Maureen-6728	1973	Montebello	Disc.

Pattern-Number	Year	Pattern-Number	Year
Monterey-4992	1954	Octavia-6669	1971
Montrosa-3053	1951	Odette-5913	1963
Montrose-6956	1974	Oliver-5254	1955
Morning Glory-5108	1954	Olivia-6987	1964
Myrna-5130	1954	Orient-5054	1958
Nadeine-8035	1951	Orleans-6024	1963
Nadya-5642	1960	Orleans-6583	1969
Namiki-B108	1972	Oxford-5767	1965
Nanarosa-4902	1953	Palomar-5354	1955
Nancy-5163	1958	Pamela-5080	1951
Nanette-4912	1953	Pamela-5172	1952
Naomi-758	1970	Pamela-7556	1974
Narnard-503	1953	Pandora-5428	1963
Nassau-7507	Disc.	Paradise-5175	1951
Natalie-5815	1970	Parklane-6961	1964
Nerrisa-5033	1950	Patricia-4982	1953
Neville-5811	1963	Patricia-7551	1974
New Amsterdam-8768	Disc.	Pauline-5686	1959
New Charm-6522	1971	Pauline-6586	1969
Newport-7506	Disc.	Pekincourt-5005	1953
Nicole-5768	1963	Penelope-4781	1952
Nicolette-6713	1972	Peony-5053	1953
Nile-6108	Disc.	Perdita-6873	1975
Nile-6719	1973	Petite-5507	1963
Nina-6667	1972	Phoenix Bird	Disc.
Ninon-6609	1973	Piccadilly-6501	1970
Nocturne-9046	1975	Piedmont-2021	1974
Nolan-5243	1955	Pinebrook-6316	1968
Nora-7546	1974	Pinecrest-6211	Disc.
Norgold-6246	1972	Pinetta-5689	1964
Norma-518	1957	Pineville-5854	1962
Norwich-5042	1956	Pink Garland-584/002	1967
Norwood-6011	1972	Pink Poppy-514	1954
Nuana-5129	1954	Pinkdawn-5352	1955
Oaklane-6310	1970	Platina-6236	1972
Oakridge-2004	1974	Plaza-B110	1964
Oakwood-5173	1952	Plymouth-6371	1968
Oceanic-8509	1976	Plymouth W/Ta-6384	1968

Pattern-Number	Year	Pattern-Number	Year
Pomona-5793	1962	Romance-6022	1972
Pompeii-6678	1974	Rosa-5460	1964
Portland	Disc.	Rosabel-5859	1962
Posy-2554	Disc.	Rosales-5790	1972
Posy-3034	1953	Rosalie-3052	1956
Prairie Gold-6514	1969	Rosaline-7537	1972
Preston-6509	1971	Rosamond-7525	1964
Prima Donna-6608	1973	Rosanne-5610	1961
Primavera-7017	1975	Roseara	Disc.
Priscilla-5310	1960	Rose Bowl-625	1968
Prunella-4990	1951	Rose Garden-5405	1958
Radcliffe-5411	1955	Roseanna-594	1967
Raleigh-5816	1962	Roseate-6729	1971
Ramona-5203	1958	Rosebud-6017	1964
Ramsey-5916	1963	Rosedale-5138	1953
Ransdell-3004	1953	Rosedawn-6467	1971
Raphael-6679	1973	Rosegai-608	1969
Ravinia-2024	1974	Roseglen-5601	1960
Redfan-4975	1953	Roselace-5041	1956
Redlace-3024	1952	Roselane-5147	1956
Regent-5681	1962	Roseline-B103	1964
Regina-5301	Disc.	Roselle-3043	1951
Regina-5442	1961	Roselle-5205	1954
Remembrance-5146	1958	Roselyn-3036	1953
Renee-5606	1960	Rosemary-5007	1953
Rengold	Disc.	Rosemead-5128	Disc.
Reverie-5431	1961	Rosemead-6210	1971
Reyrosa-6462	1968	Rosemint-6225	1969
Rialto-6014	1964	Rosemont-5048	1957
Richland-6130	1968	Rosepoint-6206	1974
Richvale-2003	1974	Rosetta-5285	1960
Ridgewood-5201	1962	Roseville-6238	1974
Rima-6906	1974	Rosewin-6584	1970
Riviera-3061	1951	Rosewood-5107	1956
Roanne-5794	1964	Rosilla-5212	1958
Roberta-6012	1964	Rosita-3037	1953
Rochelle-5805	1962	Rossina-5789	1962
Romaine-620	1974	Roxanne-6534	Disc

Pattern-Number	Year	Pattern-Number	Year
Royal Blue-2700	1974	Shelburne-5316	1960
Royal Cafe-6539	1971	Sheldon-5821	1963
Royal Claret-6537	1972	Shelley-5308	1955
Royal Mint-6538	1971	Sheridan-5441	1959
Royal Pink-5527	1960	Sherwin-6960	1964
Royce-5809	1963	Sherwood-4903	1953
Rubeta-5085	1955	Sherwood-6784	1971
Rubigold-4792	Disc.	Sheryl-6715	Disc.
Rubigold-6962	1960	Shirley-5774	1963
Ruskin-2057	1975	Sierrapine-5424	1955
Rustic-8703	Disc.	Silver Lane-6696	1972
Sabina-6461	1970	Silverdale-5594	1972
Sabrina-5590	1965	Silverster-6340	1974
Sahara	Disc.	Silverton-5569	1962
Salem-4704	1953	Silvia-6989	1964
Salisbury-9701	Disc.	Silvine-5487	1962
Samara-6422	1968	Simone-6407	1974
San Marino-5351	1955	Simplicity-7516	1964
San Saba-9030	1974	Simplicity-7533	1971
Sandra-3062	1953	Smilax-5004	1952
Santa Fe-8504	1971	Snow Pine-7517	1964
Sarasota-6852	Disc.	Snowden-6354	1970
Savoy-5825	1972	Snowflake-6951	1959
Saxony Rose-6659	Disc.	Snowville-6453	1974
Scenic	Disc.	Somerset-5317	1973
Sedgwick-2023	1975	Sonara-4711	1952
Selby-5401	1960	Sonnet-6656	1972
Selena-621	1967	Sonoda-4907	1953
Selene-7536	1972	Sonoma-6353	1971
Serenity-4952	1952	Sonora	Disc.
Seville-6521	1972	Sophia-6988	1964
Shangrila-5787	1960	Southern Glow-9005	1973
Sharlene-6933	1964	Sovereign-6808	1973
Sharon-3057	1956	Spring Blossoms-5046	1954
Shasta-2167	1975	Springdale-B105	1964
Shasta-5305	1959	St. Moritz-7511	Disc.
Shastra-2058	1975	Stafford-5919	1963
Sheila-4905	1953	Stanford-5220	1955

Pattern-Number	Year	Pattern-Number	Year
Stanley-6025	Disc.	Trevor-5780	196?
Stanton-5407	1962	Trillium-5780	Disc
Stanwood-5445	1958	Trio-6447	1968
Stanwood-9059	1975	Tropica-228	1960
Stanwyck-5818	1970	Tropica-9012	1973
Stella-6602	1973	Tudor-6046	1967
Stratford-5652	1960	Tudor Rose-6658	1971
Suffolk-7549	1973	Tuscana-3035	1953
Sugi-6030	1965	Tyrol-7543	1970
Summer Bloom-901	1972	Tyrone-6319	1967
Sunny Hill-903	1969	Vale-766	1973
Sunvilla-8704	Disc.	Valencia-5086	1955
Susanna-6242	1966	Valencia-6683	1971
Sutherland-6726	1972	Valencia-7502	Disc
Suzette-5803	1962	Valerie-5812	1967
Swansia-6854	1972	Valerie-4785	1953
Sweet Leilani-902	1969	Valiere-4981	1954
Sweet Talk-6513	1972	Vanessa-5541	1962
Sylvan-6118	1964	Verda-6355	1968
Sylvina-5945	1964	Verdon-6782	1971
Tahiti-760	1969	Vermont-6227	1965
Taianon-7509	Disc.	Verna-5140	1954
Talisman-7519	1964	Vernon-5923	1962
Tamara-4978	1953	Verona-510	1953
Tampa-6324	1966	Veronica-5009	1953
Tangiers-6803	1972	Victoria-6103	Disc
Tara-7510	Disc.	Victoria-6528	1971
Tarantella-2035	1975	Vinecourt-6694	1971
Taryn-5912	1970	Vineyard-6449	1973
Theme-5545	1963	Vintage-618	1973
Theresa-5279	1955	Viola-6711	Disc
Therese-5158	1953	Violette-3054	1953
Tilford-6712	1975	Vivian-6657	1971
Togenkyo-759	1970	Vivienne-5087	1953
Tokay-5168	1954	Vornay-4794	Disc
Toko-Ri-5786	1960	Waikiki-5145	1953
Touraine-3025	1959	Walden-2028	1971
Trent-6953	1960	Wareen-6966	Disc

SELECTED BIBLIOGRAPHY

Altman, Seymour and Violet. **The Book of Buffalo Pottery,** New York: Crown Publishers, Inc. 1969.

Brown, Raymond Lamont. "Noritake China For Those With Lean Purses". Article in **The Antiques Journal,** September 1978.

Dorn, Sylvia O'Neill. **The How To Collect Anything Book.** Garden City, New York: Doubleday & Company, Inc. 1976.

Gorham, Hazel H. **Japanese and Oriental Ceramics.** Rutland, Vermont: Charles E. Tuttle Company. 1971.

Kovel, Ralph and Terry. **Collector's Guide to Limited Editions.** New York: Crown Publishers, Inc. 1974.

Kovel, Ralph and Terry. **The Kovels' Complete Antiques Price List.** New York: Crown Publishers, Inc. 1978.

Leondorf, Gene. **Nippon Hand-Painted China.** Kansas City, Missouri: McGrew Color Graphics. 1975.

Lima, Paul and Candy. **The Enchantment of Hand Painted Nippon Porcelain.** Silverado, California: Silverado Studios. 1971.

Mebane, John. **Best Sellers In Antiques.** Dubuque, Iowa: Babka Publishing Company. 1974.

Meyer, Florence E. **The Colorful World of Nippon.** Des Moines, Iowa: Wallace-Homestead Book Company. 1971.

Munsterberg, Hugo. **The Ceramic Art of Japan.** Rutland, Vermont: Charles E. Tuttle Company. 1964.

Melvin, James and Florence, and Bourdeau, Rodney and Wilma. **Noritake Azalea China.** Danbury, Connecticut. 1975.

Robinson, Dorotha. **Nippon Hand Painted China.** Manchester, Vermont: Forward's Color Productions. 1972.

Stitt, Irene. **Japanese Ceramics of the Last 100 Years.** New York: Crown Publishers, Inc. 1974.

ABOUT THE AUTHOR

Lou Ann Donahue is a home economics graduate of Stout State University in Wisconsin. Her interest in china and the history it represents was the starting point for collecting Noritake wares of the past. This collecting has become a family hobby, with husband, Bill, and daughter, Susan, also enjoying the antiques shows and shops and the endless search for information on Noritake china collectibles. She has about 200 pieces in her private collection. As the collection grows, additions become increasingly more difficult to find but more satisfying to get. Hopefully, some of these wares will be destined for a museum in Japan.

INDEX